Travesuras en mi zoológico

ANTICS IN MY ZOO

Jacquie Ream

Illustrations by
Doina Cociuba Terrano

Book Publishers Network
P. O. Box 2256
Bothell, WA 98041
425-483-3040
www.bookpublishersnetwork.com

Copyright 2018 © Jacquie Ream
Illustrations by Doina Cociuba-Terrano
Printed in China by Amica Inc.,
05/10/2018

10 9 8 7 6 5 4 3 2 1

ISBN   978-1-945271-99-1
LCCN   2018941558

Dedication

This is dedicated to you, and those who love you.

Esto está dedicado a ti y a los que te aman.

Amelia antelope in an **a**irplane doing loop the loops! **A**lligators cleaning the **a**quarium **a**nd **a**phids in **a**prons tiptoeing **a**cross **a**n **a**ccordion! **A**ntsy **a**ardvarks in **a**erobics! **A**ll these **a**ctive **a**nimals, old and new, in my zoo!

¡Amelia antílope en un **a**vión que da vueltas y vueltas! ¡Cocodrilos limpiando el **a**cuario y pulgones en delantales caminando en puntillas **a** lo largo de un **a**cordeón! ¡**A**nsiosos osos hormigueros haciendo **a**eróbicos! ¡Todos estos **a**nimales **a**ctivos, nuevos y viejos, en mi zoológico!

Did you know?
The **aardvark** is an African mammal that hunts at night and eats insects, like ants and termites, with its long snout. (Wikipedia)

¿Sabías que...?
El oso hormiguero, o **"aardvark"** en inglés, es un mamífero africano que caza por las noches y come insectos tales como hormigas y termitas con su largo hocico. (Wikipedia)

Blathering **b**aboons! **B**allerina **b**utterflies rapping to the tune of the beaver's **b**assoon. **B**en the **b**ear is playing **b**agpipes, and the **b**arnyard **b**abies are **b**oohooing. Whatever shall I do with all these animals in my zoo?

¡Monos **b**arulleros! Mariposas **b**ailarinas cantando rap al ritmo del fagot del castor. **B**en, el oso, está tocando la gaita y los **b**ebés del corral están **b**erreando en un volumen poco armónico. ¿Qué puedo hacer con todos estos animales en mi zoológico?

B

Did you know?

The **beaver**, the second largest rodent, also a night-time worker, has front teeth that never stop growing and has good hearing, smell, and touch but poor eyesight, compensated by transparent eyelids that enable navigation underwater. (sciencekids.co.nz)

¿Sabías que...?

El castor, que en inglés se llama "**beaver**", es el segundo roedor más grande y es un trabajador nocturno. Sus dientes delanteros nunca dejan de crecer y sus sentidos del oído, el tacto y el olfato son muy buenos pero su sentido de la vista es deficiente. Para compensar por ello, tiene párpados transparentes que le permiten navegar bajo el agua. (sciencekids.co.nz).

Camels doing **c**artwheels—oh no!—smashing the **c**owboy **c**heetah's **c**heeseburger and upsetting the **c**ello of **C**aresse the **c**at! The **c**ows, **C**lara and Dorothea, are dressed in **c**andy-striped **c**ostumes while the **c**rocodile **c**roons a tune. **C**omic-book **c**haracters **c**ome parading, three by three, right on **c**ue. Let's play all day at my Alphabet Zoo!

¡Los **c**amellos están haciendo volteretas –oh, no! ¡Se están llevando por delante la hamburguesa **c**on queso del guepardo vaquero y dejando **c**aer el **c**helo de **C**aresse el gato! Las vacas, **C**lara y Dorothea, están vestidas **c**on trajes de líneas que parecen **c**aramelos mientras el **c**ocodrilo **c**anturrea una **c**anción. Las **c**aricaturas de los **c**ómics vienen en **c**aravana, de tres en tres, justo en el momento lógico. ¡Juguemos todo el día con mi abecedario del zoológico!

Did you know?
The **camel** can drink up to forty gallons of water at once. Its humps stores not water but fat that can be converted into food or water. (thefacts.com)

¿Sabías que...?
¡Los **c**amellos están haciendo volteretas –oh, no! ¡Se están llevando por delante la hamburguesa **c**on queso del guepardo vaquero y dejando **c**aer el **c**helo de **C**aresse el gato! Las vacas, **C**lara y Dorothea, están vestidas **c**on trajes de líneas que parecen **c**aramelos mientras el **c**ocodrilo **c**anturrea una **c**anción. Las **c**aricaturas de los **c**ómics vienen en **c**aravana, de tres en tres, justo en el momento lógico. ¡Juguemos todo el día con mi abecedario del zoológico! (thefacts.com)

Dolly **d**inosaur **d**ecorating the **d**ogs, **d**ucks, and **d**eer with **d**aisies and balloons. **D**affy **d**olphins on the **d**rums, **d**onkey **d**oodling **D**isney characters while playing the kazoo. All this and more at my zoo!

La **d**inosaurio **Dolly d**ecora a los perros, patos y venados con **d**alias y globos. Los **d**elfines alegres tocan los tambores, los burros **d**ibujan personajes de **D**isney mientras tocan instrumentos ecológicos. ¡Hay de todo esto y más en mi zoológico!

Did you know?

The **dinosaurs** lived on all seven continents, Africa, Antarctica, Asia, Australia, Europe, North America, and South America. The name "dinosaur" refers only to the land-dwelling reptiles that have specific traits. Dinosaurs swallowed large rocks that stayed in their stomachs to help grind up food. All dinosaurs laid eggs. Dinosaurs died out 65.5 million years ago during the Cretaceous-Tertiary period, known as the K-T event; it is thought it was due to climate change because of the dinosaurs' big farts. (factretriever.com) The blue whale is the largest animal to have lived on Earth and at 108 feet is bigger than any dinosaur. Whales and dolphins have the biggest brains of all living animals.

¿Sabías que...?

Los **dinosaurios** vivieron en los siete continentes: África, Antártica, Asia, Australia, Europa, América del Norte y América del Sur. El nombre "dinosaurio" se refiere sólo a los reptiles terrestres que tienen características específicas. Los dinosaurios engullían grandes rocas que se quedaban en sus estómagos para ayudarles a triturar la comida. Todos los dinosaurios ponían huevos. Los dinosaurios dejaron de existir hace sesenta y cinco millones y medio de años durante el período Cretáceo Terciario, conocido como el evento C-T; se cree que el suceso se produjo por el cambio climático debido a los grandes pedos expelidos por los dinosaurios (factretriever.com). La ballena azul es el animal más grande que haya vivido en la tierra y con sus treinta y dos metros es más grande que cualquier dinosaurio. Las ballenas y los delfines tienen los cerebros más grandes entre todos los animales que viven hoy en día.

E

Elephants **e**ating **e**ggplants, **e**lectric **e**els **e**xercising with **e**ight **e**ager **e**agles. **E**dison, the tiny blue **e**lf, whispers in my **e**ar, "Can we play, too, with the animals in your zoo?"

Los **e**lefantes **e**ngullen berenjenas, **e**spectaculares anguilas hacen **e**jercicios con **e**ntusiastas águilas. **É**dison, **e**l diminuto **e**lfo, susurra en mi oído **e**n un tono melódico: "¿Podemos jugar también contigo y con los animales de tu zoológico?

Did you know?
The **elephant** is the largest land animal in the world. Its trunk weighs in about four hundred pounds, has more than forty thousand muscles, and can rip out a tree by the roots or pick up a grain of rice. Elephants can cry; they have emotions and mourn for loved ones. They are frightened not by mice but by ants and bees. (list25.com)

¿Sabías que…?
El **elefante** es el animal terrestre más grande del mundo. Su trompa pesa alrededor de cuarenta y cinco kilos, tiene más de cuarenta mil músculos y así como puede arrancar un árbol de raíz, puede recoger un grano de arroz. Los elefantes pueden llorar, tienen emociones y guardan luto por sus seres queridos. Contrario a la creencia popular, se sienten atemorizados por hormigas y abejas, no por los ratones. (list25.com)

My family and I find so many things to do! We watch Ford the frog counting freckles on the fawn and five clown fish making faces at the fox playing his French horn. These are a few of my favorite friends at my Alphabet Zoo.

¡Mi familia y yo encontramos muchas cosas que hacer! Vemos a Ford la rana contando los lunares del fauno y a cinco peces payasos haciendo morisquetas al zorro quien toca su corno francés que compró a un precio módico. Estos son algunos de mis amigos favoritos en mi abecedario del zoológico.

F

Did you know?

The **fox** is more like a cat, although related to a dog, wolf, and jackal. It has the same pupils that allow for stalking prey at night; it has whiskers on its tongue, it walks on its toes and some retractable claws, and some sleep in trees like cats. It uses the earth's magnetic field to line up shadow and sound to pounce on its prey. Foxes are playful and can be domesticated pets. (mentalfloss.com)

¿Sabías que...?

Aunque se parece más al gato, el zorro (que en inglés se llama "**fox**"), está emparentado con los perros, los lobos y los chacales. Al igual que el gato, tiene pupilas que le permiten cazar a su presa por la noche y papilas en su lengua. Los zorros caminan en puntillas, tienen patas retráctiles y algunos duermen en los árboles. Utilizan el campo magnético de la tierra para registrar y alinear las sombras y los sonidos para abalanzarse sobre su presa. Los zorros son juguetones y pueden ser mascotas domesticadas. (mentalfloss.com)

Geronimo the **g**azelle and **G**lenn the **g**iraffe are playing **g**ames while the **g**orilla and **g**oose are doing **g**ymnastics with the **g**nu. So much to do at my zoo!

Gerónimo la **g**acela y Glenn la jirafa están jugando muy a **g**usto mientras el **g**orila y los **g**ansos están con el ñu haciendo **g**imnasia en un lugar bucólico. ¡Hay tantas cosas que hacer en mi zoológico!

G

Did you know?
The tallest creature in the world, the **giraffe** moves at two speeds, a walk at ten miles per hour or gallop at up to thirty-five miles per hour. NASA studied baby giraffes at birth and found out how to help astronauts avoid problems with collapsing veins in their legs when they returned to Earth. (thefactssite.com)

¿Sabías que...?
La criatura más alta en el mundo, la jirafa, **"giraffe"** en inglés, se mueve a dos velocidades: si camina, lo hace a dieciséis kilómetros por hora; si galopa, puede llegar a recorrer cincuenta y seis kilómetros por hora. La NASA estudió jirafas bebés para averiguar cómo ayudar a los astronautas a prevenir problemas con el colapso de las venas de sus piernas cuando regresan a la tierra. *(thefactssite.com)*

13

Happy Harriet the hippo, hens in hats, and helpful Helena the horse bringing honey and harmonicas home for treats. Have you ever heard of anything so sweet? So much to see and do here at my Alphabet Zoo.

Harriet, la feliz hipopótamo, gallinas que llevan sombreros y Helena la servicial yegua traen de sorpresa miel y harmónicas, ¿has escuchado alguna vez algo tan dulce, filarmónico? ¡Hay tantas cosas que disfrutar y que hacer aquí en mi zoológico!

Did you know?
The **hippo**, or hippopotamus, the "river horse," is the third largest land animal, after the white rhinoceros and elephant. It is considered the most aggressive and dangerous of animals in Africa. Its closest living relatives are whales and porpoises. (kariega.com.za)

¿Sabías que...?
El **hipopótamo** o "caballo de río" es el tercer animal terrestre de mayor tamaño. Más grandes que los hipopótamos son los rinocerontes y los elefantes. En África se les considera como los animales más agresivos y peligrosos. Sus parientes más cercanos son las ballenas y las marsopas. (kariega.com.za)

Impish **i**mpala **i**rritating Mildred the **i**bex by crunching **i**ce cubes and hiding our **i**ce cream and musical **i**nstruments in an **i**gloo! **I**magine this happening at my zoo!

Los **i**mpetuosos **i**mpalas **i**rritan a Mildred, la **i**lustre **í**bice, aplastando cubos de hielo y escondiendo nuestros helados e **i**nstrumentos musicales en un **i**glú que se convierte en un hogar sinfónico. ¡**I**magina cómo pasa todo esto en mi zoológico!

I

Did you know?

The **ibex** is a wild mountain goat found in Europe, Asia, and Africa. It is related to antelopes, buffalo, bison, cattle, and sheep. Males live in a bachelor herd, and around ten to twenty females and babies live in another group. They can jump straight up, more than six feet from a standing position. (live-science.com) The **impala,** whose name comes from a Zulu word meaning "gazelle," is a fast and graceful African antelope, clocking speeds at 60 mph. When running from prey, impalas can release a scent from the glands on their heels so the herd can stay together. (onekindplanet.org)

¿Sabías que...?

El íbice es una cabra salvaje que se encuentra en Europa, Asia y África. Es pariente de los antílopes, los búfalos, los bisontes, el ganado y las ovejas. Los machos viven en un rebaño de solteros y alrededor de diez a veinte hembras y sus críos viven en otro grupo. Pueden saltar más de dos metros sin tener que tomar impulso (livescience.com). Los impalas, cuyo nombre deriva de una palabra Zulu que significa "gacela", son antílopes rápidos y elegantes que llegan a alcanzar velocidades de hasta noventa y seis kilómetros por hora. Cuando huyen de sus depredadores, pueden desprender de las glándulas en sus talones un aroma que ayuda a que la manada pueda seguir unida. (onekindplanet.org)

J

Jabbering Jackal and jumping Jesse the jackrabbit climbing on the jumbo jungle gym. Not one or two but all the animals have fun at my zoo!

JUMBO JUNGLE GYM

El chacal parlanchín y Jesse la liebre veloz escalan en el gigante gimnasio de la jungla. ¡No sólo uno o dos, sino todos los animales se divierten con gozo en mi zoológico!

¿Sabías que...?
El chacal, que en inglés se llama "**jackal**", está emparentado con el perro, el zorro, el coyote y el lobo, y vive principalmente en África. Cada grupo de chacales tiene un ladrido con un sonido particular que sólo es reconocible por los miembros de la misma familia. El chacal rayado puede ulular como un búho. (livescience.com)

Koalas in ketchup-stained kerchiefs looking in kaleidoscopes as Ali's kids bounce on kettledrums and scare all the kangaroos. This way, that way, in all directions at my zoo!

Los koalas llevan pañuelos manchados con kétchup mientras ven a través de caleidoscopios cómo los niños de Ali rebotan en los timbales y asustan a todos los canguros. ¡De esta manera, de la otra, con movimientos fantásticos en mi zoológico!

Did you know?
The **koala** is not a bear; it is a marsupial like a kangaroo, which means the young are born immature and develop in a pouch. It lives only in Australia, eats only eucalyptus leaves, and sleeps in trees during the day. It is a relative of the wombat and kangaroo. (ohfact.com)

¿Sabías que...?
El **koala** no es un oso, es un marsupial como el canguro, es decir, los bebés nacen prematuramente y terminan de desarrollarse en un pliegue de la piel de la madre que forma una especie de bolsa que sirve como incubadora. El koala sólo vive en Australia, se alimenta únicamente con hojas de eucalipto y duerme en los árboles durante el día. Está emparentado con los canguros y los tejones australianos. (ohfact.com)

Llamas singing lullabies and lambs listening. Leopards doing laundry and Mary lion writing letters while Lincoln the llama picks up litter. Not a lazy crew, the animals at my zoo!

Mientras las llamas cantan canciones de cuna, los corderos escuchan. Los leopardos lavan la ropa y Mary, la leona, escribe cartas en tanto que Lincoln, la llama, recoge la basura. ¡No son un grupo perezoso, los animales de mi zoológico!

L

Did you know?
The **llama** comes from South America and is used as a pack animal. It is a relative of the camel. Its hair is wool and is used in fabric, rugs, and ropes. A llama will stick its tongue out if it is mad at you. It will also hiss and spit. (mentalfloss.com, softschools.com)

¿Sabías que...?
La **llama** es oriunda de América del Sur y se usa como un animal de carga. Es pariente del camello. Su pelaje es lana y se utiliza en telas, alfombras y cuerdas. Si las llamas están bravas contigo, te sacan la lengua. También escupen y silban. (mentalfloss.com, softschools.com)

There are **m**onkeys into **m**ischief. Bill, Paul, Steve, Larry, Jeff, **M**ark, and Lawrence are putting **m**arbles in the popcorn **m**achine. The **m**ouse is **m**ad at the **m**ean **m**ongoose for **m**aking a **m**ess of his **m**eal. The **m**ares read **m**agazines aloud, and the **m**uskrat **m**imes do **m**agic tricks for the **m**oose. All this hullabaloo at my zoo.

Hay **m**onos traviesos. Bill, Paul, Steve, Larry, Jeff, **M**ark y Lawrence están poniendo **m**etras en la **m**áquina de palomitas de **m**aíz. El ratón está enfadado con la **m**alvada **m**angosta por haber hecho un desastre con su comida. Las yeguas leen revistas en voz alta y las ratas almizcleras hacen **m**ímica y trucos de **m**agia para el alce. ¡Todo este auténtico alboroto en **m**i zoológico!

Did you know?
Muskrats are large rodents, native to North America, related to the rat, mouse, vole, gerbil, hamster, and lemming. They build lodges of cattails and vegetation. Their paddle-like feet make swimming backwards possible. (livescience.com)

¿Sabías que…?
Las ratas almizcleras, que en inglés se llaman **"muskrats"**, son grandes roedores, nativos de América del Norte, que están emparentados con las ratas, ratones, ratones de campo, jerbos, hámsteres y otros roedores. Construyen sus madrigueras con una planta de hojas que parecen espadas y otra vegetación. Sus patas, que son como aletas, hacen que les sea posible nadar al revés. (livescience.com)

Naughty, noisy nightingales in a nest, fighting with one another. Newborns in the nursery crying for their mothers, such a to-do! Nine nice neighbors, Martin Luther, Jonas, Edna, Sylvia, Emily, Henry David, Ralph Waldo, TS, and Walt feed all the babies in my zoo!

Pícaros y bulliciosos ruiseñores pelean los unos con los otros en un nido. Los recién nacidos en la guardería, lloran por sus madres, ¡tantas cosas que hacer! ¡Nueve vecinos amables, Martin Luther, Jonas, Edna, Sylvia, Emily, Henry David, Ralph Waldo, T.S. y Walt dan de comer con arrojo a los animales de mi zoológico!

Did you know?
The male **nightingale** sings best at night. The name means "night songstress." It is the national bird of Iran. (lifestyle.iloveindia.com)

¿Sabías que...?
El ruiseñor en inglés se llama **"nightingale"**. Es por las noches cuando se puede escuchar el mejor canto de los machos de esta especie. Su nombre significa "cantante de la noche" y es el pájaro nacional de Irán. (lifestyle.iloveindia.com)

27

Oprah, the **o**ne **o**ctopus from the **o**cean, plays the **o**boe for William the **o**tter as Sandra the **o**wl tells a story for the **o**celot and **o**thers. Listen and you, too, will hear many interesting tales at the zoo!

Oprah, la pulpo del **o**céano, toca el **o**boe para William la nutria, mientras la búho Sandra cuenta una historia al **o**celote y a **o**tros. ¡Escucha, y tú también, **o**irás interesantes cuentos en el zoológico!

Did you know?
The **octopus** can recognize your face. It has three hearts. It will eat its arms when bored. It can use tools and open a childproof bottle. (livescience.com, *Seattle Times*)

¿Sabías que...?
El pulpo, que en inglés se llama **"octopus"**, puede reconocer tu cara. Tiene tres corazones y cuando está aburrido se come sus tentáculos que son como sus brazos. Puede usar herramientas y hasta abrir recipientes a prueba de niños. (livescience.com, *Seattle Times*)

P

Edgar the **P**anda **p**aints **P**anther with **p**olka dots as **p**enguins **p**lay the **p**iano. **P**igs recite **p**oetry, **p**leasing the **p**olar bears, **p**uppies, **p**arrots, and **p**eople, too. **P**retty **p**urple **p**igeons coo, and everyone is happy at the Alphabet Zoo!

El oso **p**anda Edgar **p**inta **p**anteras con lunares al mismo tiempo que los **p**ingüinos tocan el **p**iano. Los cerdos recitan **p**oesía, lo cual complace a los osos **p**olares, a los cachorros, a los loros y a las **p**ersonas también. ¡Bonitas **p**alomas **p**úrpuras emiten un arrullo y todos son felices en el mágico alfabeto del zoológico!

Quizzing **q**ueen bee Ella **q**uickly **q**uestions **Q**uail while **q**uipping **Q**uahog removes porcupine **q**uills from his shell. **Q**uacking ducks announce the news to all of us at my Alphabet Zoo.

La excéntrica abeja reina Ella, rápidamente le hace preguntas a Codorniz, mientras la ocurrente almeja se **q**uita de su concha las púas del puercoespín. Los patos anuncian con sus graznidos las noticias para todos nosotros en mi alfabeto del zoológico.

Did you know?
The **quahog** is a clam, the official shellfish of the state of Rhode Island. Its name comes from the Narragansett Native Americans, who used the shells as wampum, or shell beads for necklaces, bracelets, or belts. Clams don't have brains. (woodsman.com)

¿Sabías que...?
Lo que en inglés se llama **"quahog",** es en español almeja redonda o americana y es el marisco oficial del estado Rhode Island. Su nombre proviene de la tribu de los nativos americanos llamada Narragansett quienes usaban las conchas como elementos de adorno para collares, pulseras o cinturones. Las almejas no tienen cerebro. (woodsman.com)

Roosters Daniel and Davy crow about the rodeo round-up. Reindeer, rabbits, and red robins race to the barnyard to watch raccoons riding rhinos. Rowdy shouts of "yahoo!" can be heard in every corner of my zoo!

Los gallos Daniel y Davy cacarean acerca del final del rodeo. Venados, conejos y petirrojos hacen carreras hacia el establo para ver a los mapaches montando rinocerontes. ¡Se oyen "¡yahoo!" y gritos eufóricos en cada esquina de mi zoológico!

R

Did you know?
The **rhino**, or **rhinoceros**, is the second largest land animal and an herbivore, eating fruit, grasses, and foliage from African and Asian forests and grasslands. Its name means "horn nose." If the horn breaks off, the rhino can grow another one. The horn is the same stuff as human fingernails and hair. (todayifoundout.com)

¿Sabías que…?
El **rinoceronte** es el segundo animal terrestre de mayores dimensiones. Es herbívoro, come frutas, grama y vegetación de las selvas y praderas de Asia y África. Su nombre significa "nariz de cuerno". Si su cuerno se rompe puede volver a crecer ya que está compuesto por los mismos elementos que se encuentran en las uñas y cabello de los humanos (todayifoundout.com).

Maya, Abagail, and Jonas make a **s**crapbook of **s**illy **s**nakes and **s**nails, **s**erious **s**quirrels, **s**piders **s**pinning, and a little **s**omething about everyone, large and **s**mall. No one can be **s**ad, that's for **s**ure, so bring a **s**mile with you to my Alphabet Zoo!

Maya, Abigail y Jonás hacen un álbum de recortes de **s**erpientes tontas y caracoles, ardillas **s**erias, arañas hilando, y un poco de cada cosa acerca de todos, grandes y pequeños. ¡Ciertamente nadie puede estar triste, así que trae una **s**onrisa contigo, amigo, a mi alfabeto del zoológico!

S

Did you know?
The **squirrel** can smell food buried a foot in snow. It will pretend to bury a nut to fool a thief. The hind legs of a squirrel are double-jointed. The eyes are situated so the squirrel can see behind it. A squirrel can leap twenty feet. Only Australia and Antarctica have no squirrels. (thefactsite.com)

¿Sabías que...?
En inglés, la ardilla se llama **"squirrel"**. Estos animales pueden oler la comida hasta cero punto tres metros bajo la nieve. Para despistar a los ladrones de su comida, les hace creer que entierra sus nueces. Las patas traseras de las ardillas tienen articulación doble. Sus ojos están situados de forma tal que las ardillas pueden ver detrás de sí y pueden saltar hasta seis metros. Los únicos lugares en los que no hay ardillas son Australia y Antártica. (thefactsite.com)

Tickled **T**oad **t**ouches her **t**oes while Mae C. **t**he **t**urkey in a **t**urban **t**akes her **t**ime and Neil **t**he **t**urtle avoids **t**raffic in a **t**axi **t**o come see **t**wo **t**igers on TV. **T**hey **t**hank you for being here at my Alphabet Zoo!

El divertido sapo **t**oca sus dedos mientras Mae C., el pavo que lleva un **t**urbante, se **t**oma su **t**iempo y la **t**ortuga Neil **t**rata de escapar del **t**ráfico en un **t**axi para venir a ver a dos **t**igres en la **t**elevisión. ¡Ellos **t**e agradecen por estar aquí en mi alfabeto del zoológico!

T

Did you know?
The **turkey** is related to the T. rex and velociraptor. It sleeps in trees. Ben Franklin wanted the turkey to be America's symbol instead of the eagle. (livescience.com)

¿Sabías que...?
El pavo, que en inglés de llama **"turkey"**, es pariente del tiranosaurio y del velociraptor y duerme en los árboles. Ben Franklin quería que el símbolo de Estados Unidos fuese el pavo en vez del águila. (livescience.com)

Look **u**p! Frank and Jane the **u**nicorns on **u**nicycles balancing **u**mbrellas! What a sight for **u**s! **U**seful, too, when it rains at my zoo!

¡Mira hacia arriba y verás a Frank y a Jane, los **u**nicornios, montando monociclos mientras balancean paraguas! ¡Qué hermosa vista para nosotros! ¡Además es también **ú**til su movimiento acrobático cuando llueve en mi zoológico!

Did you know?

The **unicorn,** a mythical creature, has been recorded as early as the fifth century BCE. Marco Polo thought they were "ugly brutes," not realizing he had seen rhinos. Since 1971, Lake Superior State University in Sault St. Marie, Michigan, has issued hunting permits for unicorns. (mentalfloss.com)

¿Sabías que...?

El **unicornio** es una criatura mítica cuya existencia se registra desde tan temprano como el quinto siglo antes de Cristo. Marco Polo pensaba que eran "bestias toscas", sin darse cuenta de que había visto rinocerontes. Desde 1971 la Universidad del Estado del Lago Superior en Sault Ste. Marie, Michigan, ha emitido permisos para cazar unicornios. (mentalfloss.com)

Debby the **v**eterinarian came today, bringing **v**egetables and a **v**acuum cleaner for the **v**ain **v**ampire bat and a **v**elvet **v**alentine for the **v**ulture who was **v**ery sad to have lost his **v**aluable heart. *"Merci beaucoup,"* said the French hen, and everyone agreed it was a happy day at the zoo!

La **v**eterinaria Debby **v**ino hoy y trajo **v**egetales y una aspiradora para el **v**ano murciélago **v**ampiro y un regalo del día de San **V**alentín forrado en terciopelo para el buitre, quien estaba muy triste por haber perdido su **v**alioso corazón. ¡"Merci beaucoup", dijo la gallina francesa, y todos estuvieron de acuerdo en que era un día feliz y hermoso en el zoológico!

Did you know?

The **vulture** is being studied by scientists because of its formidable senses and abilities to find bodies from crimes. There is an International Vulture Awareness Day, celebrated the first Saturday of September, to educate people on how interesting and valuable vultures are. (thespruce.com)

¿Sabías que...?

El nombre del buitre en inglés es **"vulture"**. Los científicos están estudiando a este animal por sus formidables sentidos y la habilidad que tienen para encontrar cuerpos de personas que han sido víctimas de un crimen. El primer sábado de septiembre es la fecha en la que se celebra el Día Internacional de Concienciación sobre el Buitre y se educa a la gente sobre lo interesantes y valiosos que son estos animales. (thespruce.com)

The **w**hite **w**olf **w**inks at the **w**izard, a clue to **w**ake the **w**hole zoo to see the **w**hales **w**ashing **w**indows with lots of sudsy **w**ater, **w**hile **w**acky Herman the **w**alrus makes **w**affles for everyone. **W**ho in the **w**orld **w**ouldn't enjoy breakfast at my Alphabet Zoo?

El lobo blanco le guiña el ojo al hechicero, es una señal para despertar a todo el zoológico para que vean a las ballenas lavando las ventanas con grandes cantidades de agua espumosa. Al mismo tiempo, la estrafalaria morsa Herman, hace gofres para todos. ¿Quién en el mundo no disfrutaría un desayuno dichoso en mi alfabeto del zoológico?

Did you know?
The **wolf** would rather hide than bark at a stranger. A wolf runs on its toes. Compared to you with five million scent cells, a wolf has two hundred million. With webs in between the toes, a wolf can swim up to eight miles. Wolves communicate with distinctive facial expressions. (factretriever.com)

¿Sabías que...?
"Wolf" en español se llama lobo. Es un animal que prefiere esconderse antes de ladrarle a un extraño, corre en puntillas y en comparación con tus cinco millones de células olfativas, el lobo tiene doscientos millones. Como tiene membranas interdigitales en sus patas, el lobo puede nadar hasta doce kilómetros. Los lobos se comunican con particulares expresiones faciales. (factretriever.com)

45

X, the unknown, stole the **x**ylophone from Stanley, and everyone was in a stew. **X** was sorry; he had a party and invited everyone at the zoo!

X, el desconocido, robó el **x**ilófono de Stanley y todos estaban nerviosos. **X** estaba arrepentido, hizo una fiesta y, como es lógico, ¡invitó a todos los animales del zoológico!

Did you know?
X is an unknown factor in math. The **xylophone** is a percussion musical instrument. The wooden bars are arranged somewhat like a piano, each one a different length. No one knows the origins of the xylophone, but it is found in the early recorded histories of Melanesia, Southeast Asia, Europe, and Africa. (OUPblog, oup.com)

¿Sabías que...?
X es un factor desconocido en matemáticas. El **xilófono** es un instrumento musical de percusión. Las barras de madera están dispuestas en una manera muy similar a las teclas del piano y cada una tiene una longitud diferente. Nadie conoce los orígenes del xilófono, pero se han encontrado registros de su existencia en historias de Melanesia, el sureste de Asia, Europa y África (OUPblog, oup.com).

Langston, the **y**oung, **y**awning **y**ak is eating **y**ams, **y**ellow potatoes, and lemon **y**ogurt, toying with his **y**o-**y**o. How rude! **Y**ou wouldn't do that, would **y**ou? What is the best time of day to play in the **y**ard? **Y**esterday morning, **y**ou say, when the grass was wet with dew and we had waffles at the zoo!

Langston, el joven **y**ak que bosteza constantemente, está comiendo ñames, papas amarillas **y y**ogur de limón mientras juega con su **y**oyo, ¡cuán descortés! Tú no harías eso, ¿cierto? ¿Cuál es el mejor momento para jugar en el patio? ¡Tú dices que ayer en la mañana, cuando la grama estaba mojada por el rocío y comimos gofres deliciosos en el zoológico!

Did you know?

The **yak** is a relative of the buffalo and bison. It lives at the highest altitude of any mammal. A yak uses its horn to break through snow for food and to defend itself. A yak can survive cold of −40 degrees Fahrenheit. Yaks grunt but do not moo. (softschools.com)

¿Sabías que...?

El **yak** es pariente del búfalo y del bisonte. Es el mamífero que vive en los sitios más altos. El yak usa sus cuernos para abrirse paso en la nieve en búsqueda de comida y para defenderse. El yak puede sobrevivir a temperaturas tan bajas como a cuarenta grados centígrados bajo cero. Los yaks no mugen, gruñen. (softschools.com)

Zero to zillions, lots of numbers in the universe! Zesty Betsy zebra counts all day, zipping zippers and zig-zagging through a maze. Come along with me; you must see all these zany creatures from A to Z. Spend a day or two at my Alphabet Zoo!

¡De cero a chorrocientos, hay montones de números en el universo! La enérgica zebra Betsy hace cuentas todo el día, cerrando cierres y haciendo zigzag a través de un laberinto. Ven conmigo, debes ver a todas estas criaturas chifladas de la "A" a la "Z". ¡Pasa uno o dos días históricos en mi alfabeto del zoológico!

Z

Did you know?
The zebra is a speed demon, outrunning most of its predators with speeds of 65 mph or more. The stripes, like fingerprints, are unique to each zebra and act as camouflage for the individual and in the herd. Also, stripes visually confuse flies and other biting insects. In ancient Rome, trained Grévy's zebras pulled chariots at circuses, billed as "horse-tigers." (discoverwildlife.com)

¿Sabías que...?
La zebra es extremadamente veloz y puede dejar atrás a la mayoría de sus depredadores porque puede correr a velocidades de más de ciento cuatro kilómetros por hora. Sus rayas, que son como huellas dactilares, son únicas en cada una de ellas y sirven como un mecanismo de camuflaje tanto individualmente como para la manada entera. Asimismo, las rayas confunden visualmente a las moscas y otros insectos que pican. En la Roma antigua había zebras Grévy's o zebras imperiales que son las más grandes, que eran entrenadas para halar las carrozas en los circos y se les llamaba "caballos-tigre." (discoverwildlife.com)

Famous Americans in Antics in My Zoo

Here's a little bit of history, and if you can imagine, animals can be people, too! Come meet them at my zoo!

A: Amelia Earhart (antelope) was the first woman pilot to fly across the Atlantic.

B: Benjamin Franklin (bear) was a Founding Father and man of many talents.

C: Clara Barton and **Dorothea Dix** (striped cows) were Civil War nurses. **Caresse Crosby** (cat with cello) held the first patent for the modern bra.

D: Dolly Parton (dinosaur) is a singer, songwriter, multi-instrumentalist, record producer, actress, author, businesswoman, and philanthropist. **Walt Disney** was a pioneer and major influence in the movie industry in animation and cartoons.

E: Thomas Edison (man behind the books), "The Wizard of Menlo Park," is said to be America's greatest inventor. He created the phonograph, motion picture camera, and a practical electrical light bulb, as well as contributed to inventions that would modernize the industrial world, holding over one thousand patents in the United States and globally.

F: Henry Ford (frog), inventor of the assembly-line technique of mass production for his Ford Motor Company's first affordable Model T, with interchangeable parts, revolutionized the American way of life.

G: Geronimo (gazelle) was a Native American leader and medicine man of the Apache tribe. **John Glenn** (giraffe) was the first NASA astronaut to orbit the Earth and was a United States senator.

H: Helena Rubinstein (horse), businesswoman and founder of the cosmetics company Helena Rubinstein Incorporated, was known also as an art collector and philanthropist. **Harriet Beecher Stowe** (hippo) was an abolitionist and the author of *Uncle Tom's Cabin*. **Harriet Tubman** (hippo), an abolitionist and escaped slave herself, guided others to freedom through a network known as the Underground Railroad.

I: Mildred "Babe" Didrikson Zaharias (impala) was one of the most decorated female athletes in track and field.

J: Jesse Owens (jackrabbit), four-time Olympic gold medalist in track and field, was one of the greatest athletes of the twentieth century.

K: Muhammad Ali (kangaroo), professional boxer, is considered one of the most influential and controversial sports figures of the twentieth century.

L: Mary Lyon (lion) was the founder of the first women's college, Mt. Holyoke Female Seminary. **Abraham Lincoln** (llama) was the sixteenth president of the United States.

M: Bill Gates and **Paul Allen** of Microsoft, **Steve Jobs** and **Steve Wozniak** of Apple, **Larry Page** of Google, **Mark Zuckerberg** and **Sheryl Sandberg** of Facebook, and **Lawrence Roberts** of the internet (all monkeys) are giants of the modern technological revolution.

N: Martin Luther King, civil rights leader, **Edna St. Vincent Millay, Sylvia Plath, Henry David Thoreau, Ralph Waldo Emerson, T. S. Eliot,** and **Walt Whitman** are seven great poets and writers (and with the two anonymous friends make nine neighbors).

O: Oprah Winfrey (octopus), "Queen of All Media," is multi-talented and best known for her successful career as talk show hostess of the *Oprah Winfrey Show*. William (otter) is for two authors, **William Styron** and **William Faulkner**. **Sandra Day O'Connor** (owl) was the first woman Supreme Court justice.

P: Edgar Allen Poe (panda), poet and writer, is known best for his stories of mystery and the macabre.

Q: Ella Fitzgerald (queen bee) was a superb singer, known as "Queen of Jazz."

R: Daniel Boone and **Davy Crockett** (roosters) were American frontiersmen and explorers.

S: Jonas Salk developed the first successful vaccine for polio. **Maya Angelou** is a poetess. **Abagail Adams**, a major influence and voice for women, advocated for inclusion of women in the drafting the Constitution of the United States.

T: Mae C. Jemison (turkey) was the first African American NASA astronaut.

U: Frank Lloyd Wright (unicorn) was a renowned architect. **Jane Adams** (unicorn), "mother of social work," was the first American woman to be awarded the Nobel Peace Prize.

V: Debby Turner (veterinarian) is a talk show host and veterinarian.

W: Herman Melville (whale) was the author of *Moby Dick*.

X: Stan Lee is the founder of Marvel Comics.

Y: Langston Hughes (yak) is a celebrated poet, famous for a new art form, jazz poetry.

Z: Betsy Ross (zebra) made the first American flag.

Estadounidenses famosos en *Travesuras en mi zoológico*

He aquí un poco de historia y, si lo pueden imaginar, ¡los animales pueden ser personas también! ¡Ven a conocerlos en mi zoológico!

A: Amelia Earhart (antílope) fue la primera mujer piloto que cruzó el Atlántico volando.

B: Benjamin Franklin (oso) fue uno de los padres de la patria y un hombre de muchos talentos.

C: Clara Barton y **Dorothea Dix** (vacas con rayas) fueron enfermeras durante la Guerra Civil. **Caresse Crosby** (gata con el chelo) fue la propietaria de la primera patente para el sostén moderno.

D: Dolly Parton (dinosaurio) es una cantautora que toca múltiples instrumentos y es además productora musical, actriz, escritora, mujer de negocios y filántropa. **Walt Disney** fue pionero y una de las más influyentes figuras en la industria cinematográfica en las áreas de animación y caricaturas.

E: Se dice que **Thomas Edison** (el hombre tras los libros), "El mago del parque Menlo", es el más grande inventor estadounidense. Él fue el creador del fonógrafo, la cámara de imágenes en movimiento y un práctico bombillo eléctrico, así como también contribuyó en la invención de artefactos que modernizarían el mundo industrial. Fue dueño de más de mil patentes en Los Estados Unidos y a nivel global.

F: Henry Ford (rana), dueño de la compañía Ford Motor, fue el inventor de la línea automática de ensamblaje para la producción masiva de su carro Modelo T, un vehículo asequible y de partes intercambiables que revolucionó el estilo de vida estadounidense.

G: Gerónimo (gacela) fue un líder indígena de Estados Unidos y hombre de medicina, perteneciente a la tribu Apache. **John Glenn** (jirafa) fue el primer astronauta de la NASA que orbitó la tierra y fue senador de Los Estados Unidos.

H: Helena Rubinstein (yegua), mujer de negocios y fundadora de la compañía de cosméticos Helena Rubinstein Inc., también fue conocida como coleccionista de arte y filántropa. **Harriet Beecher Stowe** (hipopótamo) fue activista por la abolición de la esclavitud y la autora de *La cabaña del tío Tom*. **Harriet Tubman** (hipopótamo), quien fue esclava cimarrona, también luchó a favor de la abolición de la esclavitud y guió a otros hacia la libertad a través de una red conocida como el Ferrocarril Subterráneo.

I: Mildred "Babe" Didrikson Zaharias (impala) fue una de las atletas con mayores reconocimientos en pista y campo.

J: Jesse Owens (liebre) ganó la medalla de oro olímpica en las competencias de pista y campo en cuatro ocasiones y fue uno de los más grandes atletas del siglo veinte.

K: Muhammad Ali (canguro), boxeador profesional, es considerado una de las figuras deportivas más influyentes y controversiales del siglo veinte.

L: Mary Lyon (león) fue la fundadora de la primera escuela de estudios superiores para mujeres, llamado Seminario Femenino Mt. Holyoke. **Abraham Lincoln** (llama) fue el décimo sexto presidente de Los Estados Unidos.

M: Bill Gates y **Paul Allen** de Microsoft, **Steve Jobs** y **Steve Wozniak** de Apple, **Larry Page** de Google, **Mark Zuckerberg** y **Sheryl Sandberg** de Facebook y **Lawrence Roberts** de internet (todos los monos), son gigantes de la revolución tecnológica moderna.

N: Martin Luther King -líder de los derechos civiles-, **Edna St. Vincent Millay**, **Sylvia Plath**, **Henry David Thoreau**, **Ralph Waldo Emerson**, **T.S. Eliot** y **Walt Whitman** son siete grandes poetas y escritores (y con los dos amigos anónimos, suman nueve vecinos).

O: Oprah Winfrey (pulpo), "Reina de todos los medios", es una mujer multifacética y es extensamente conocida por su exitosa carrera como presentadora de su programa de entrevistas llamado *El show de Oprah Winfrey*. William (nutria) es por dos autores a saber: **William Styron** y **William Faulkner**. **Sandra Day O'Connor** (búho) fue la primera mujer en la Corte Suprema de Justicia.

P: Edgar Allan Poe (oso panda), poeta y escritor, es ampliamente conocido por sus historias macabras y de misterio.

Q: Ella Fitzgerald (abeja reina) fue una extraordinaria cantante conocida como "La reina del Jazz".

R: Daniel Boone a **Davy Crockett** (gallos) fueron colonizadores y exploradores estadounidenses.

S: Jonas Salk desarrolló la primera vacuna contra el polio que fue exitosa. **Maya Angelou** es una poetisa. **Abigail Adams**, una de las figuras más influyentes y defensora de las mujeres, luchaba por la inclusión de las mismas en el proceso de redacción de la Constitución de Los Estados Unidos.

T: Mae C. Jemison (pavo) fue la primera astronauta afroamericana en la NASA.

U: Frank Lloyd Wright (unicornio) fue un reconocido arquitecto. **Jane Adams** (unicornio), "madre del trabajo social", fue la primera mujer estadounidense a quien se le otorgó el Premio Nobel de la Paz.

V: Debby Turner (veterinaria) es presentadora de un programa de entrevistas y veterinaria.

W: Herman Melville (ballena) fue el autor de *Moby Dick*.

X: Stan Lee es el fundador de los cómics Marvel.

Y: Langston Hughes (yak) es un celebrado poeta, famoso por la poesía jazz, una nueva forma de arte.

Z: Betsy Ross (zebra) hizo la primera bandera estadounidense.